THIS BELONGS TO: